I Like Stripes
Me gustan las rayas

by Deborah Schecter

ISBN: 978-1-338-70290-3
Illustrated by Anne Kennedy
Copyright © 2020 by Deborah Schecter. All rights reserved.
Published by Scholastic Inc., 557 Broadway, New York, NY 10012

10 9 8 7 6   68   23 24 25 26/0

Printed in Jiaxing, China. First printing, June 2020.

A candy cane has stripes.
I like stripes.

El bastón de caramelo tiene rayas.
Me gustan las rayas.

Toothpaste has stripes.
I like stripes.

La pasta dental tiene rayas.
Me gustan las rayas.

A flag has stripes.
I like stripes.

La bandera tiene rayas.
Me gustan las rayas.

A zebra has stripes.
I like stripes.

La cebra tiene rayas.
Me gustan las rayas.

A street has stripes.
I like stripes.

La calle tiene rayas.
Me gustan las rayas.

A ladybug has stripes.
No! No! No!

La mariquita tiene rayas.
¡No! ¡No! ¡No!

A ladybug has spots.
I like spots!

La mariquita tiene lunares.
¡Me gustan los lunares!